Essential Audition So

male Vocalists *broadway*

	page no.	on the CD	vocal range
Don't Get Around Much Anymore Sophisticated Ladies	9	**Track 2**	
Get Me To The Church On Time My Fair Lady	2	**Track 1**	
If I Were A Rich Man Fiddler On The Roof	16	**Track 4**	
It Don't Mean A Thing **(If It Ain't Got That Swing)** Sophisticated Ladies	12	**Track 3**	
It's All Right With Me Can-Can	25	**Track 5**	
The Lady Is A Tramp Babes In Arms	38	**Track 8**	
On The Street Where You Live My Fair Lady	30	**Track 6**	
Thank Heaven For Little Girls Gigi	34	**Track 7**	
Wand'rin' Star Paint Your Wagon	50	**Track 10**	
With A Little Bit Of Luck My Fair Lady	44	**Track 9**	

Series Editor: Anna Joyce

Editorial, production and recording: Artemis Music Limited

Design and Production: Space DPS Limited

Published 2001

IMP

International MUSIC Publications

RESPECT THE VALUE OF MUSIC

Get Me To The Church On Time
from *My Fair Lady*

Words by Alan Jay Lerner
Music by Frederick Loewe

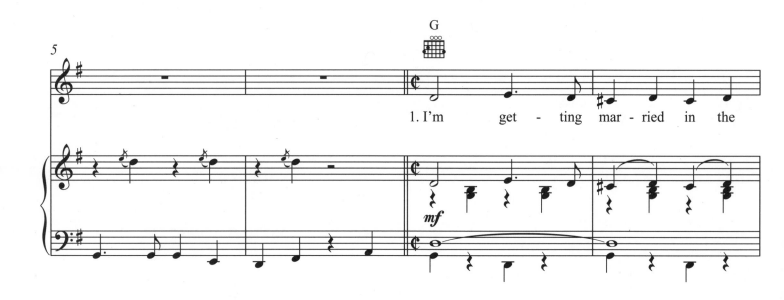

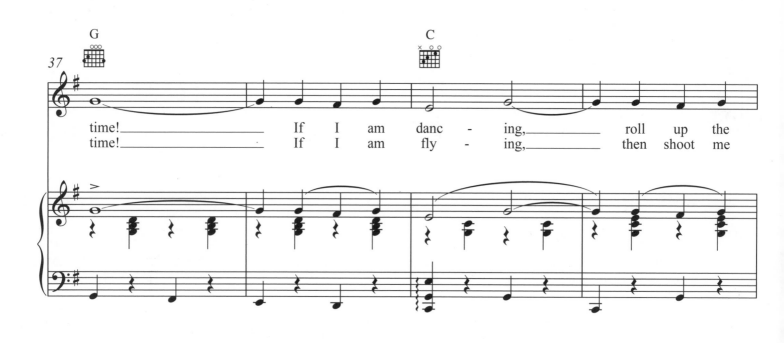

Don't Get Around Much Anymore

from *Sophisticated Ladies*

Words by Bob Russell
Music by Duke Ellington

Backing

It Don't Mean A Thing
(If It Ain't Got That Swing)
from *Sophisticated Ladies*

Words by Irving Mills
Music by Duke Ellington

Backing

If I Were A Rich Man
from *Fiddler On The Roof*

Words by Sheldon Harnick
Music by Jerry Bock

C
11
would-n't have to work hard, dai-dle, dee-dle, dai-dle, dig-guh, dig-guh, dee-dle, dai-dle, dum.
loco
G7 Cm D7(b9)/A G7 Cm
15
To Coda
(Tacet)
6fr
If I were a bid-dy, bid-dy rich, dai-dle, dee-dle, dai-dle, dai-dle man. I'd build a
rall.
Quasi rubato
Fm Bb7/F Ebmaj7 Gm7(b5) C7
19
2fr
big tall house with rooms by the doz-en right in the mid-dle of the town, a
Fm G7 C C7
23
2fr
fine tin roof with real wood-en floors be-low. There would be

It's All Right With Me
from *Can-Can*

Words and Music by Cole Porter

Track 5
Backing

It's the wrong time_____ and the wrong place,_____ tho' your

face is charm - ing it's the wrong face,_____ it's not

On The Street Where You Live
from *My Fair Lady*

Words by Alan Jay Lerner
Music by Frederick Loewe

Thank Heaven For Little Girls

from *Gigi*

Words by Alan Jay Lerner
Music by Frederick Loewe

The Lady Is A Tramp
from *Babes In Arms*

Words by Lorenz Hart
Music by Richard Rodgers

Moderately

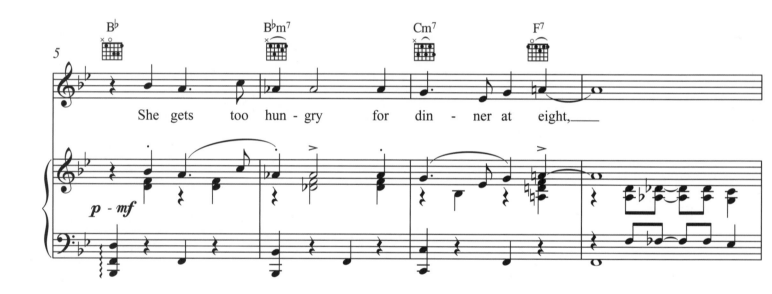

She gets too hun-gry for din-ner at eight,____

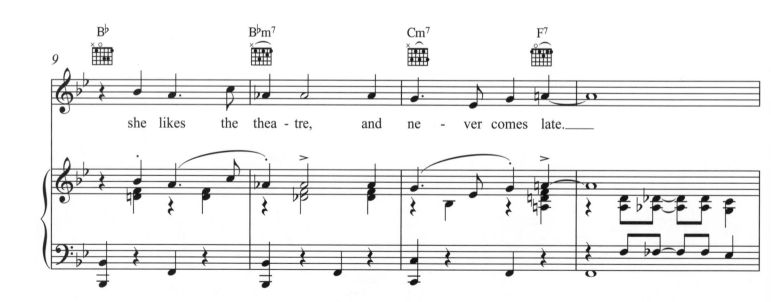

she likes the thea-tre, and ne-ver comes late.____

Backing

With A Little Bit Of Luck
from *My Fair Lady*

Words by Alan Jay Lerner
Music by Frederick Loewe

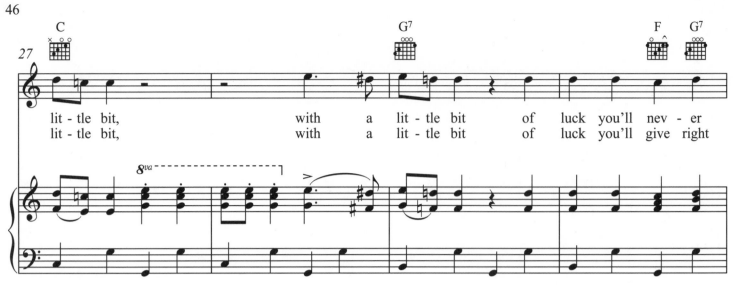

lit - tle bit, with a lit - tle bit of luck you'll nev - er
lit - tle bit, with a lit - tle bit of luck you'll give right

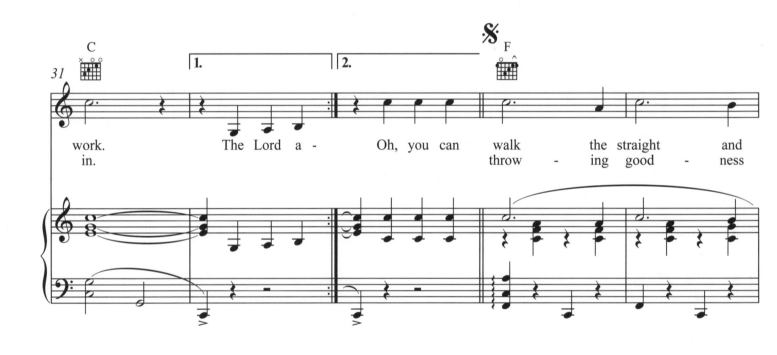

work. The Lord a - Oh, you can walk the straight and
in. throw - ing good - ness

nar - row,_____ but with a lit - tle bit of luck you'll run a -
at you;_____ but with a lit - tle bit of luck a man can

mok! The gen - tle sex was made for man to mar - ry,_____
duck! The Lord a - bove made man to help his neigh - bour,_____

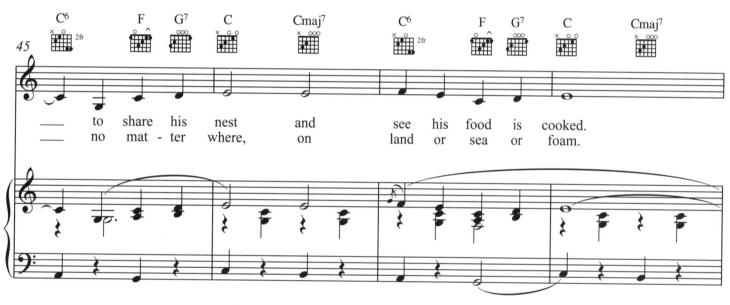

_____ to share his nest and see his food is cooked.
_____ no mat - ter where, on land or sea or foam.

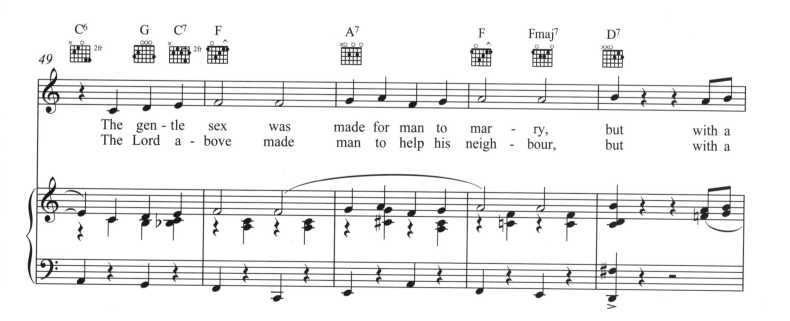

The gen - tle sex was made for man to mar - ry, but with a
The Lord a - bove made man to help his neigh - bour, but with a

Wand'rin' Star
from *Paint Your Wagon*

Words by Alan Jay Lerner
Music by Frederick Loewe

8861A PVC/CD

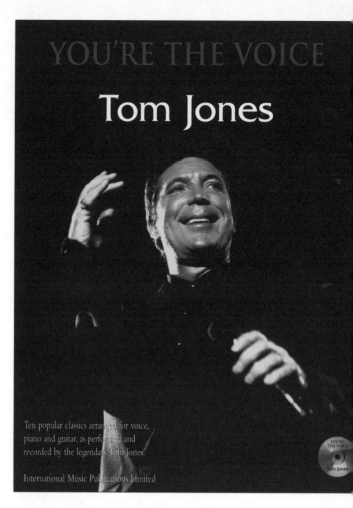

8860A PVG/CD

Casta Diva from Norma - Vissi D'arte from Tosca
Un Bel Di Vedremo from Madam Butterfly - Addio,
Del Passato from La Traviata - J'ai Perdu Mon
Eurydice from Orphee Et Eurydice - Les Tringles
Des Sistres Tintaient from Carmen - Porgi Amor
from Le Nozze Di Figaro - Ave Maria from Otello

Delilah - Green Green Grass Of Home - Help
Yourself - I'll Never Fall In Love Again - It's Not
Unusual - Mama Told Me Not To Come - Sexbom
Thunderball - What's New Pussycat - You Can
Leave Your Hat On

YOU'RE THE VOICE

The outstanding new vocal series from IMP
CD contains full backings for each song, professionally arranged to recreate the sounds of the original recording